Foundation Spelling

Guidelines

Catherine Hilton
Margaret Hyder

MCH Publications

Contents

Introduction

The materials

These photocopiable materials are designed for:

- young people in Years 10, 11, 12 or 13;
- 16 -19 year old college students;
- adults in education, training or work.

The materials are sufficiently flexible to be used in a variety of learning situations: class/group sessions; open or distance learning.

Tutor information

This book forms part of a series of books intended to help students who lack confidence in their own spelling ability or who are encountering difficulties with other study areas because of poor spelling. It can be used as support material for students on a wide range of courses.

Foundation Spelling - Guidelines

The worksheets in this book introduce students to the most useful spelling rules. We have tried to express the rules governing spelling in a simple way and to break them down into easy learning steps. Students are given examples of everyday words that follow the guidelines. At times, we have included everyday exceptions to the guidelines but we have omitted any exceptions that we feel would confuse students or are words that are unlikely to be used regularly by students.

Used in conjunction with other books in the series, students will have access to worksheets that cover the most common spelling difficulties. We do not suggest that students work systematically through this or any other book in the series. Some students may only need to work through certain worksheets which cover the rules with which they encounter difficulties. The worksheets have been arranged in groups and we advise that students should work through each group in the order the sheets appear in the book. Initially, students should work through pages 3 - 6 so that they have an understanding of the language that is used in the guidelines throughout the worksheets; pages 8 - 11 cover rules for one, one, one words; pages 12 - 15 cover words ending in silent 'e'; pages 18 -25 deal with rules for words ending in 'y'; pages 27 - 29 deal with rules for two syllable words; and pages 33 - 35 cover 'ie' / 'ei' words.

At the bottom of some of the sheets there is an arrow symbol which directs students to other related sheets they should move on to.

Tutors should encourage students to build up a portfolio of these spelling sheets to use as a reference source and to include the Student Guide in their portfolios.

Photocopying

The worksheets may be photocopied provided they are used solely in your own institution. If you wish to photocopy for any other purpose, you must gain permission from *MCH Publications*.

© 1996 *MCH Publications*   ISBN 1 898901 12 0

Published by *MCH Publications*, PO Box No. 3720, Redditch, Worcestershire. B97 5EF
Cover design by Vivienne Weatherill Oddy.
Printed by Bloomfield Ltd, 7b Waterloo Industrial Estate, Bidford-on-Avon, Warwickshire. B50 4JH

For further information or to place an order, telephone (01386) 870825 / 792755.

Student Guide

The first four units, 'Vowels', 'Consonants', 'Base words' and 'Syllables' help you understand the terms we use throughout the worksheets.
Work through these four units first. Make certain you understand each of these worksheets and have successfully completed the activities before you move on.

The arrow symbol acts as a signpost.
At the bottom of some worksheets you will see this symbol

This shows you which worksheet or worksheets you should move on to. We group together some worksheets. Make certain you work through these sheets in the order of the page numbers. For example, pages 18 - 25 deal with words that end in 'y'. Start this group of worksheets on page 18 and work through.

We advise you to keep all your spelling sheets in a folder.
You can then remind yourself of the guidelines when you need them.
It would help to keep this information sheet in your folder too.

Practise the words that cause you problems.
Follow the advice we give in each **Hint**.

Build up your own personal dictionary.
Put in any words that you frequently use and have problems spelling.

If you don't know the meaning of a word in a worksheet, use a dictionary to look up the word.
Sometimes the dictionary explanation of a meaning can be difficult to follow so look up the meaning in another dictionary. If you still don't understand, ask your tutor for help.

You can use the answers to check your work.
Where you have been asked to use words in sentences, you will need to ask your tutor to check your work.

Vowels

In many of the worksheets in this book, we will mention
vowels.
There are **26** letters in the alphabet and **5** of these are
vowels.

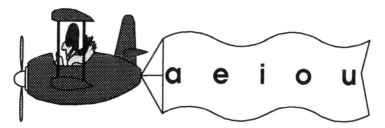

Each vowel has a **short vowel sound**.

a as in **a**dd
e as in **e**gg
i as in **i**tch
o as in **o**range
u as in **u**gly

Vowels also have a **long sound**. This sound is the same as the name of the letter:

    a as in **a**pron   **e** as in **e**qual   **i** as in **i**ce   **o** as in **o**pen   **u** as in **u**nit

It is often the vowels that give us problems when we spell words because:
► In some words vowels don't make the sound you would expect.
    Example   pretty   -   '**e**' makes a short '**i**' sound
► Vowels can also join together to make a different sound.
    Example   head   -   '**ea**' makes a short '**e**' sound

Over to you

The vowels in the words below are missing. Use the clue beside each word to work out the word and then fill in the missing letters.

c _ n f _ s s	admit	f _ n _ s h	complete
d r _ n k	a beverage	c l _ c k	tells the time
l _ n g t h	opposite of width	s h _ p h _ r d	looks after sheep
_ d _ l t	not a child	m _ r d _ r	kill unlawfully
_ l p h _ b _ t	26 letters	c _ n n _ t	or can't
c _ r n _ r	a bend	f _ n t _ s t _ c	wonderful
s m _ l l	a scent	s h _ c k _ n g	terrible
c _ b w _ b	made by a spider	l _ t t _ r	a written message

Consonants

▶ There are **21** consonants in the alphabet (all the letters that aren't vowels).

▶ A consonant usually has the same sound regardless of which word it is in or its position in a word.

Hint

♦ Some consonants can join with:

> other consonants
> vowels

and then their sound changes.

Examples

    1. You hear '**t**' in '**t**ot' and '**h**' in '**h**ot' but when '**t**' and '**h**' join together, they make a new sound in words like

> '**th**is' and '**th**at'.

    2. When '**o**' and '**w**' join together, they can make a long

> '**o**' sound as in '**ow**n'.

♦ '**y**' can have a consonant sound as it does at the beginning of words.
Examples

         yes   **y**acht   **y**ellow

♦ '**y**' can have a vowel sound in some words.
Examples

    fr**y**   d**y**e suppl**y**   ver**y**   safel**y**

          sounds like '**I**'   sounds like '**ee**'

Over to you

Some of the consonants in these words are missing. Put in the correct consonants. You may need to use a dictionary to check any words you are uncertain about.

y e s _ e r d a _	q u i c _	c o r _ e c _
w o _ k i n g	g _ a t e f u _	a l _ o w
s e p a _ a _ e	b u r _ l a r	b e g i n _ i n _
w e _ c o m e	w o _ d e r _ u l	p o p u _ a r
t a k e _	d i _ l i k e	f u _ u r e
b r o u _ _ t	p o s _ i b _ e	a c _ e p _
d i f _ e r e n _	d a _ g e r	c h i l _ r e _

Base words

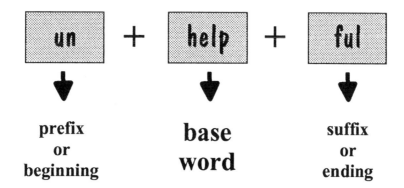

This word is made up of **3** parts.

| prefix or beginning | base word | suffix or ending |

► A **base word** is a word without any prefixes or suffixes added to it.

► In the worksheets in this book you will be:
* adding beginnings and endings to **base words**
* learning guidelines for what happens to **base words** when prefixes or suffixes are added

Over to you

prefixes	dis	im	mis	un					
suffixes	able	ed	er	ful	ing	ly	ment	ness	some

Above are the range of beginnings and endings which have been added to base words to form the words in the table below.
Take off these prefixes and suffixes and you will be left with the base words.
Highlight each base word.

forgetful	weighing	dryness
quarrelsome	enjoyment	misspell
unprofitable	unnecessary	impolite
listener	disobeyed	dissatisfy
limited	unemployment	lively
commitment	applying	madness
regretful	destroyer	equally

Syllables

► A syllable is a sound part.

► A syllable always has at least one vowel (**a**, **e**, **i**, **o**, **u**) in it. Remember, '**y**' can act as a vowel too.

► A word may be made up of 1, 2, 3, 4 or even more syllables.

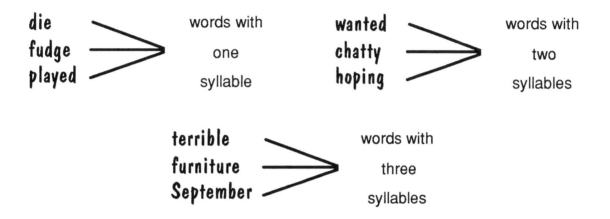

die
fudge
played → words with one syllable

wanted
chatty
hoping → words with two syllables

terrible
furniture
September → words with three syllables

► You can hear how many syllables a word has.
► Listen for one sound to end and another begin in this two syllable word.

cur / tain

You will hear: **cur**   (first syllable)

tain   (second syllable)

Over to you

Say aloud each of the words in the box below. Beside each word, write the number of syllables the word has.

share	managing	family	every
between	finally	wonderful	sandwich
placing	cancel	destination	occur
pole	prefer	want	simple
chimney	supper	slippery	factory
responsible	claim	tomorrow	foreign

Adding prefixes

► These are all prefixes:

il	un	im	mis	auto	bi	re	ir
in	sub	dis	ex	con	anti	sur	pre

► A prefix is a group of letters which you add to the beginning of a word to change its meaning.

Examples

un + natural = unnatural ('**un**' means 'not' so 'unnatural' means 'not natural')

bi + cycle = bicycle ('**bi**' means 'two' so 'bicycle' is a cycle with two wheels)

Hint

It's easy adding prefixes.
- Usually you just add the prefix to the beginning of the word.
- The spelling of the word doesn't change.
  The spelling of the prefix doesn't change.
  Example   im + possible = impossible
- Remember:
       if the **last** letter of the prefix
       is the same as the **first** letter of the word
       the new word will have a double letter in it.
  Examples   im + **m**oral = im**m**oral
                 ir + **r**esponsible = ir**r**esponsible

Over to you

Add the prefix at the top of each box to each word in that box. Write the 'new' word. If you are uncertain about the meaning of a word, check it in a dictionary.

im		re		un	
mature		appear		aware	
modest		arrange		certain	
patient		assure		named	
polite		fuel		necessary	
practical		issue		tidy	
probable		print		usual	

One, one, one words

► You will need to study this page which helps you to be aware of **one**, **one**, **one** words before you work through pages **9**, **10** and **11**.

1. How many syllables?

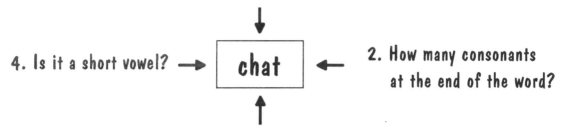

4. Is it a short vowel? → chat ← **2. How many consonants at the end of the word?**

3. How many vowels before the final consonant?

Your answers should be:
* 'chat' has **one** syllable
* 'chat' ends in **one** consonant ('**t**')
* 'chat' has **one** short vowel ('**a**') before the '**t**'

► Such words are often called **one**, **one**, **one** words.
> **one** syllable
> **one** final consonant
> **one** short vowel

Over to you

To practise 'spotting' **one**, **one**, **one** words, highlight the **one**, **one**, **one** words in the box below.

Before you start, it may be helpful to remind yourself about vowels, consonants and syllables by checking pages **3**, **4** and **6**.

drop	hug	cool	meet	shut	more
bank	bring	thrill	work	racket	tread
record	win	slid	top	want	clap
snap	swim	prevent	strap	trip	floor
nudge	direct	small	join	cross	result
dream	travel	trim	crash	slim	stop

 Now work on pages **9**, **10** '**Doubling a consonant**'.

Doubling a consonant

► All the words on this worksheet follow the **one**, **one**, **one** pattern.

> **one** syllable
> **one** final consonant
> **one** short vowel before the final consonant

Examples

spot   drop   shut   big   trip

► What happens to the '**t**' in 'spot' when we add a suffix beginning with a **vowel** or a '**y**'?

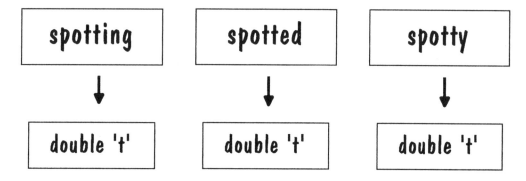

spotting	spotted	spotty
↓	↓	↓
double 't'	double 't'	double 't'

Hint

♦ Double the final consonant of the base word when you add a **vowel** suffix or a '**y**' to a base word which has:

> **1** syllable
> **1** final consonant
> **1** short vowel before the final consonant

Examples

slip + ed = sli**pp**ed
fog + y = fo**gg**y
sit + er = si**tt**er

♦ As well as remembering this guideline, you could also learn such words by splitting the word between the double consonant and stressing each consonant.

Example

planning
pla**n** / **n**ing

say 'pla<u>n</u>'   say '<u>n</u>ing'

Doubling a consonant

Over to you

1) Match each beginning in Box 1 to an ending from Box 2. Write the complete word in Box 3. Each word you make will have a double consonant in it.

Box 1	Box 2	Box 3
strip	ning	
thin	mer	
sad	ny	
dim	per	
spin	der	
sun	red	
scar	test	
wet	nest	

2) Add the suffix to each base word below and write the new word. Don't forget to follow the guidelines given in the **Hint**.

scrub + ing		step + ing	
fat + en		drag + ing	
pad + ed		mud + y	
slap + ing		slim + er	
rip + ed		jam + ed	
skin + y		wit + y	
win + er		grip + ed	
drop + ed		grin + ed	
wet + er		trap + ing	

 There is more about adding suffixes to **one**, **one**, **one** words on page **11**.

No change

► On pages **9, 10** '**Doubling a consonant**' you saw that you have to **double** the final consonant when you add a **vowel** suffix to words with:
* **one** syllable
* **one** final consonant
* **one** short vowel before the final consonant

Examples

sad + est = sa**dd**est   swim + ing = swi**mm**ing

► These suffixes begin with a **consonant**.

ly	ness	ful	less

► Does the '**d**' in 'sad' double when we add '**ly**' or '**ness**'?

sa**d**ly	sa**d**ness

Hint

• When you add a suffix beginning with a **consonant** to a base word which has:

    one syllable
    one final consonant
    one short vowel before the final consonant

you **don't double** the final consonant of the base word.

Over to you

dimly	brimful	spotless	strapless	madness	skinless

Match each word from the box above to its clue. Write the correct word beside the clue.

without a mark   _____

no straps   _____

opposite of brightly   _____

without a skin   _____

extreme foolishness   _____

full to the top   _____

Dropping an 'e'

| hope | I was | hoping | to go shopping. |

| excite | Shabbir is an | excitable | child. |

| spice | She likes | spicy | food. |

► In each of the examples above we have shown you:

a base word ending in a silent 'e'

| hope | excite | spice |

and added to it a suffix beginning with a vowel or a 'y'

| ing | able | y |

► What happens to the silent 'e' at the end of the base word?

| hoping | excitable | spicy |

► The silent 'e' is dropped.

Hint

- When you add:
    a suffix beginning with a vowel ('**a**', '**e**', '**i**', '**o**', '**u**') or a '**y**'
    to a base word which ends in a silent '**e**'
    that '**e**' is usually dropped.

Examples

$$\text{arriv}\textbf{e} + \textbf{al} = \text{arrival}$$
$$\text{confus}\textbf{e} + \textbf{ing} = \text{confusing}$$
$$\text{admir}\textbf{e} + \textbf{able} = \text{admirable}$$

- This guideline works for nearly all silent '**e**' words.

Dropping an 'e'

Over to you

1) Add these suffixes ('**ing**' and '**er**') to each base word below. Write the words you have made in the correct columns.

base word	+ ing	+ ed
grate		
close		
arrange		
use		
chase		
arrive		
decide		
enquire		
provide		
advise		
vote		
sneeze		
dance		

2) For each sentence below, choose the correct spelling from each pair of words and write it in the space.

a. She was going _____ with toothache. (crazey / crazy)

b. I keep _____ my temper with him. (losing / loseing)

c. They're so _____ . (noisy / noisey)

d. John's _____ to marry her hurt her pride. (refuseal / refusal)

e. The artist found the view _____ . (inspiring / inspireing)

f. The ground is very _____ . (stoney / stony)

g. Bill is so _____ . (lazey / lazy)

h. Stop _____ water! (wasting / wasteing)

i. Helen's _____ is almost impossible to read. (writing / writeing)

 There is more about adding suffixes to silent 'e' words on pages **14, 15**.

Keeping an 'e'

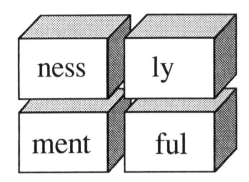

► In the boxes above each suffix starts with a **consonant**:

n in 'ness'   **l** in 'ly'   **m** in 'ment'   **f** in 'ful'

► What happens to the silent 'e' at the end of the base words below when a suffix beginning with a **consonant** is added?

| forgiv**e** | + | **n**ess | = | forgiv**e**ness |

| hop**e** | + | ful | = | hop**e**ful |

| lat**e** | + | ly | = | lat**e**ly |

Hint

* When you add
    a suffix beginning with a **consonant**
    to a word which ends with a silent '**e**'
    keep the '**e**'.

Examples

care + less = careless
safe + ly = safely

* There are, however, a few everyday words which drop the silent '**e**' when we add certain **consonant** suffixes.

Useful examples

argu**e** + **m**ent = argument (no '**e**' before '**m**ent')
nin**e** + **t**h = ninth (no '**e**' before '**t**h')
tru**e** + **t**h = truth (no '**e**' before '**t**h')
tru**e** + **l**y = truly (no '**e**' before '**l**y')

Try to remember these words.

Keeping an 'e'

Over to you

nameless	safety	hopeless	grateful
bravely*	amusement*	lonely*	blameless
placement	completely*	politeness	hateful
sincerely	careful*	excitement	ninety*

1) Sort the words from the box above into groups according to their endings:
less, **ty**, **ful**, **ment**, **ness**, **ly**.
Write each word on the correct card below.

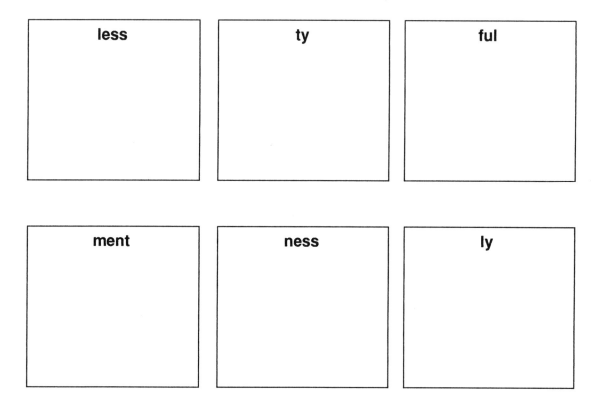

2) Now use each word from the box marked with a * in a separate sentence.

Review

► In this worksheet you have added **consonant** suffixes to words that end in a silent 'e'.

> Keep the 'e' with a **consonant** suffix.

► On pages **12**, **13** you added **vowel** suffixes to words ending in a silent 'e'.

> Drop the 'e' with a **vowel** suffix.

Ending in 'ly'

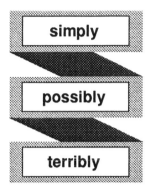

simply

possibly

terribly

► What sound do you hear at the end of 'simp**ly**', 'possib**ly**' and 'terrib**ly**'?
► The '**lee**' sound you hear is made by the letters '**ly**'.

Hint

- When a base word ends in '**le**'
  and has the suffix '**ly**' or '**y**' added to it
  we hear a '**lee**' sound at the end.

Examples
  gent**le** + **ly** = gent**ly** (we drop the '**le**' when we add '**ly**')
  bubb**le** + **y** = bubb**ly** (we drop the '**e**' when we add '**y**')
- Remember:
  This '**lee**' sound you hear is made by the letters '**ly**'.

Over to you

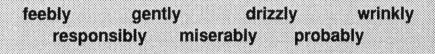

feebly   gently   drizzly   wrinkly
responsibly   miserably   probably

Use one of the words from the box above in each of these sentences. Use each word once.

a. The weather is damp and _____ .

b. She acted very _____ by calling the fire brigade.

c. The lizard's skin was dry and _____ .

d. Having lost his job, John walked _____ from his office.

e. Today is _____ the best day of my life.

f. The injured cat struggled _____ as the vet examined it.

g. She picked up the newborn baby _____ .

'lly' endings

▶ Sometimes the ending of words like those opposite cause problems.

▶ You may be uncertain whether such words end in '**ly**' or '**lly**'.

▶ You cannot hear which ending is correct.

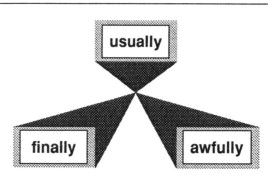

Hint

* Words which already end in '**l**' will end '**lly**' when the suffix '**ly**' is added.
  Examples

usual	+	**ly**	=	usua**lly**
final	+	**ly**	=	fina**lly**
awful	+	**ly**	=	awfu**lly**

* The reason is:
  the base word ends in '**l**'
  the suffix begins with '**l**'
  so
  the 'new' word will have '**ll**' before the '**y**'

Over to you

1) Add '**ly**' to each of these base words and write the new word in the second box.

beautiful

local

actual

fatal

gradual

total

general

dreadful

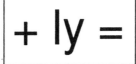

2) Now use each word you have made in a separate sentence.

The letter before 'y'

► Words ending in 'y' can cause problems when you add suffixes to them.
► What you do depends on the letter before the final 'y'.

| enjoy |
| key |
| delay |
| survey |

a vowel before the final 'y'

| family |
| lorry |
| fly |
| supply |

a consonant before the final 'y'

On pages **19 - 25**, you will be following the guidelines for adding suffixes to words ending in 'y' that have:

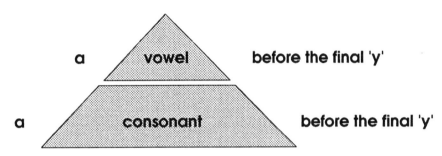

a **vowel** before the final 'y'

a **consonant** before the final 'y'

In this worksheet you will practise looking at words ending in 'y' and being aware of the letter before the final 'y'.

Over to you

1) Highlight all the words in the box below that have a **vowel** before the final 'y'.

easy	buy	obey	lazy	necessary
pray	bury	try	satisfy	employ
annoy	injury	boy	mystery	dry
happy	play	valley	forty	victory

2) Use each word with a **consonant** before the final 'y' in the sentences below. Use each word once.

    a. _____ to bring the washing in as soon as it is _____.

    b. Laura was _____ to be _____ this birthday.

    c. The exam won't be _____ for her as she is so _____.

    d. James must _____ his fans despite his ankle _____.

    e. It's _____ to _____ the evidence.

    f. His _____ was a _____ to his trainer.

 Now work through pages **19** to **25** to find out more about words ending in 'y'.

A vowel before 'y'

► All the base words on this worksheet have a **vowel** before the final '**y**'.
► We will add suffixes that:

begin with a vowel	begin with a consonant
Examples able er ant ing ed or	*Examples* ful ment ty

word	+	ending	=	new word
delay	+	ed	=	delayed
employ	+	ment	=	employment
obey	+	ing	=	obeying
joy	+	ous	=	joyous

Hint

♦ Look for words with a **vowel** before the final '**y**'. These words are easy.
♦ Write the word and add the suffix.
♦ It doesn't matter if the suffix begins with:
    a **vowel**
    or a **consonant**.

Over to you

Each ending below is numbered.

1. able	2. ant	3. ed	4. er	5. ful	6. ing	7. ment	8. or	9. ty

Beside each base word in the table below is the number of the ending you should add to the word. Write the new word in the table.

word	ending	new word	word	ending	new word
obey	3		play	5	
destroy	4		buy	6	
royal	9		employ	1	
pray	4		buoy	2	
enjoy	7		survey	8	

A consonant before 'y'

► All the words on this worksheet have a consonant before the final 'y'.
► You will be adding:

        vowel endings   *examples*   ed   age

        consonant endings   *examples*   ness   ly

Hint

◆ Examples of words with a consonant before the final '**y**'

        ha**pp**y   ca**rr**y

◆ When you add:

        a vowel ending

        or a consonant ending

    change '**y**' to '**i**' before adding the ending.

◆ *Examples*   happy   happily   happiness

           carry   carries   carried   carrier   carriage

◆ This works for all endings except '**ing**'.

   You will find out about adding '**ing**' on page **21**.

Over to you

Here are some endings you could add to the words below.

es	**ly**	**able**	**er**
ness	**ed**	**age**	**ous**

You will not be able to add all the endings to every word. See how many endings you can add to each word. When you write the new words, remember to change '**y**' to '**i**' before adding an ending. Each word must be a real word. The first one is done for you.

marry	marries	married	marriage		
tidy					
easy					
lazy					
steady					
copy					
study					
fury					
empty					
heavy					

'ing' is different

► All the base words in this worksheet have a consonant before the final '**y**'.
► We are adding '**ing**' to all these words.

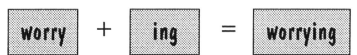

Don't change '**y**' to '**i**'   **Do** keep '**y**' and add '**ing**'

Hint

- Adding '**ing**' to words with a consonant before the final '**y**' is different from adding other endings.
- Keep '**y**' and add '**ing**'.
- There are 2 reasons for this.
   1. No English word has '**ii**' together.
      If we changed '**y**' to '**i**' and added '**ing**', there would be '**ii**'.
                worri**ing**   worrying
   2. **cop** / **y** has 2 sound parts or syllables.
      cop / **y** / **ing** has 3 sound parts or syllables.
      The '**y**' forms a sound part.
      You need to keep the '**y**' before adding '**ing**' otherwise a sound part would disappear.

Over to you

Use the clues to help you unscramble the words in the table below. Each word ends in '**ing**'. Write the word in the last column.

nevying	being jealous of	
eryquing	questioning	
upyoccing	living in	
ingdeny	not admitting	
ingyfl	moving through the air	
hrruying	going quickly	
tasisfying	pleasing	
plysuping	providing with	
lperingy	answering	
appingyl	making a request for a job	

Plurals - ends in 'y', add 's'

singular
one person or thing

plural
more than one

► Most of the time when we want to make a word plural, we add 's'.

Example

 one clock   two clocks

Hint

- When we want to make words that end in 'y' plural, we look at the letter before the final 'y'.
- If it is a **vowel** before the final 'y', it's easy - just add 's'.

Examples

boy**s**   donkey**s**   abbey**s**

- The guidelines are the same for making such words plural as for adding other endings. (See page **19**.)

Over to you

Find the answer to each clue to complete the wordsquare.
All the words for the answers are plurals ending in the same pattern:
a **vowel**, then 'y', then 's'.

1. rest from work or studies
2. smoke comes out of these
3. they ride horses
4. low areas between hills
5. long-tailed animals in trees
6. a pair of organs in the body
7. used by trains
8. travelling from one place to other places
9. these make you late
10. seen in 'Wild West' films

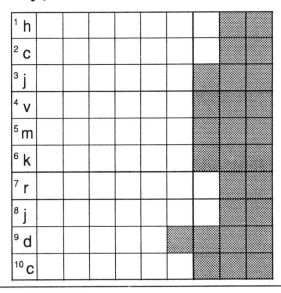

Plurals - changing 'y' to 'i'

lorry
baby
family
story

► Highlight the letter before the final 'y' in each word on the notice board above.

Hint

- Each word on the notice board above has a **consonant** before the final '**y**'.
- When you want to make such words plural, you must:
  - change '**y**' to '**i**'
  - and add '**es**'.
- When you follow these guidelines, the words above become:
  lorr**ies**   bab**ies**   famil**ies**   stor**ies**

Over to you

1) Write the plural of each of these words.

body	party	mystery
city	property	century
bully	factory	opportunity
sky	supply	charity

2) Use the clues to complete these words. Each word ends in '**ies**'.

autumn fruits	b _ r r _ _ _	books are kept here	l _ b r _ r _ _ _
amounts	q u a _ _ _ t _ _ _	made up of soldiers	a _ m _ _ _
things you do	a c _ _ v _ t _ _ _	annoying insects	f _ _ _ _
carry passengers across water	f _ r r _ _ _	France, England, India are --------	c o u _ _ r _ _ _
not your friends	e n _ m _ _ _	another word for women	l _ d _ _ _

Does 'y' change to 'i'?

▶ In this worksheet you will be able to try out all the guidelines you have worked with on pages **19** to **23**.

Hint

♦ When words end in '**y**', always check the letter before the final '**y**'.
♦ If there is a **vowel** before the final '**y**', just add the ending.
> This rule applies for making words plural too.
♦ If there is a **consonant** before the final '**y**', change '**y**' to '**i**' and then add your ending.
> This works for making words plural too.
> It works for all endings except '**ing**'.
♦ When you want to add '**ing**' to words with a **consonant** before the final '**y**', keep the '**y**' and just add '**ing**' to the word.
♦ For the tricky words that don't follow the guidelines, see page 25.

Over to you

1) Write the plurals for each of these words.

turkey	gangway	county
twenty	birthday	hobby
pastry	enquiry	victory

2) Add the ending or endings in brackets beside each word and then write the new words in the space beside.

survey (ed, ing, or)	
pretty (er, est, ness)	
glory (ous)	
display (ed, ing)	
carry (ed, er, ing)	
apply (ed, ing)	
delay (ed, ing)	
happy (ly, ness)	
lazy (ly, ness)	
necessary (ly)	
convey (ed, ing, or)	

Tricky 'y' words

► These are some of the tricky words that don't follow the guidelines for words ending in 'y'.

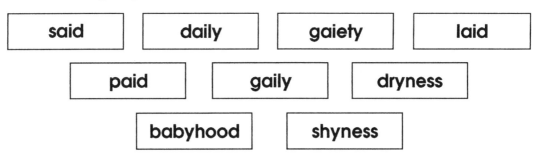

said	daily	gaiety	laid

paid	gaily	dryness

babyhood	shyness

Hint

◆ Group words with a similar pattern together.

say	saying	*but*	**said**
lay	laying	*but*	**laid**
pay	paying	*but*	**paid**

◆ Group together these rhyming words too.

dry   sly   shy

dry	dryly	dryness
sly	slyly	slyness
shy	shyly	shyness

Over to you

paid	babyhood	daily	dryness	laid	said

Use one word from the box above to replace the underlined word or words in the sentences below. Use each word once. The word you choose should have the same meaning as the underlined word or words it replaces.

a. Sean went to the gym <u>each day</u>.

b. Nasreen <u>told me</u> she had <u>handed in the money for</u> her rent.

c. Mr Brewster <u>placed</u> his keys on the table.

d. His mother always told embarrassing stories about his <u>time as a baby</u>.

e. The <u>dry patch</u> was caused by always having his hands in water.

Adding 'ed'

► What's the difference between these two sentences?

       I open the door. (I am doing this now.)

       I open**ed** the door. (I have already done this.)

► We have added '**ed**' to '**open**' in the second sentence. This shows that the action happened in the past.

► You may have difficulties with words that end in '**ed**' because you can't hear the '**ed**' clearly at the end.

---

opened   borrowed   showed   swirled

You probably only hear the '**d**' - the '**e**' appears to be silent.

---

dashed   fetched   sniffed   attacked

You probably only hear a '**t**' sound at the end.

---

wanted   counted   attended   roasted

You may hear an '**id**' sound at the end.

Hint

♦ With words that end in '**ed**':

    Ignore what you hear.

    Think about what you're doing to the word.

    The action has happened so add '**ed**'.

♦ It will help you to remember the spelling if, as you write the word, you change the way you say it.

Example

    count**ed**   (stress '**ed**' to rhyme with '**Ted**')

Over to you

Unscramble these words. All the words end in '**ed**'.

p e n e d h a p	h	r e e d t u r n	r
t e d l i s	l	c r e d a s h	c
e d k b o o	b	a l k t e d	t
n e d d r o w	d	e a n c l e d	c
n e d e d e	n	a m p e d s t	s

Single or double?

▶ All the words on this worksheet have 2 syllables or sound parts.

com / mit	pre / fer	cred / it

▶ Each word ends in the same pattern:

one short vowel
one consonant

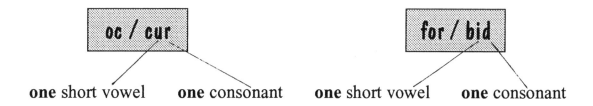

one short vowel   **one** consonant   **one** short vowel   **one** consonant

We will be adding endings which begin with a **vowel**.
Examples   **able**   **ed**   **en**   **er**   **ing**

Card 1 no change	Card 2 change
limit + **e**d = limited number + **ing** = numbering listen + **er** = listener profit + **a**ble = profitable	forget + **ing** = forgetting submit + **ed** = submitted forbid + **en** = forbidden recur + **ing** = recurring

You will notice that:
▶ In Card 1 we **don't double** the last letter when we add on a **vowel** suffix.
▶ In Card 2 we **double** the final consonant when we add on a **vowel** suffix.

Adding on a **consonant** suffix isn't a problem.
You just add the **consonant** suffix to the base word.
You don't double the final consonant.

Examples
commit + **m**ent = commitment forget + **f**ul = forgetful allot + **m**ent = allotment regret + **f**ul = regretful

Single or double?

Over to you

1) Add the ending by the side of each word and then write the new word. Listen for the stress and follow the guidelines.

budget + ing	admit + ance
offer + ed	limit + ed
submit + ing	transfer + ing
begin + er	prefer + ed
orbit + ed	order + ing

2) Highlight the correct spelling from each of these pairs of words. Check any of the words you are uncertain about in your dictionary.

beginning	begining	creditted	credited
admited	admitted	forbidding	forbiding
referred	refered	regretable	regrettable
commited	committed	omitting	omiting
entering	enterring	occurred	occured

 Words ending in **'l'** are different. Now work on page **29**.

'l' is different

► All the base words in this worksheet have a similar pattern.

* 2 syllables
* end in a single 'l'
* have a short vowel before the final 'l'

Example

la / bel

* 2 syllables
* one final 'l'
* one short vowel ('e') before final 'l'

Hint

◆ When you add a **vowel** suffix to:
   a 2 syllable word
   ending in 'l'
   double the final 'l' before you add your vowel ending.
   Examples   travel - travelled travelling traveller

◆ If you add a **consonant** suffix, **don't** double the final 'l'.
   Example   quarrel + **s**ome = quarrelsome

◆ A point to remember - if you add the vowel endings '**ity**' or '**ise**',
   you don't double the final 'l' e.g. reality   finalise

Over to you

1) Use the clues to unscramble these words. Each word will have a '**ll**' before the vowel ending.

s i g l l n a e d	s	e d l l c e c a n	c
v e m a r l l o u s	m	a l l i n g p e d	p
e r l l t r a v e	t	e d l l p a t r o	p
e d l l t o t a	t	m o i n g d e l l	m
i n g l l q u a r r e	q	l l i n g l a b e	l

2) Use a dictionary to check the meaning of each of the words below. Ask your tutor for help if you don't understand the dictionary explanations.
                appal compel excel propel repel
3) Now add '**ed**' or '**ing**' to each word and use it in a sentence.

Plurals - add 'es'

Shopping List	Shopping List
5 _pens_	3 rabbit _hutches_
2 _tins_ of white paint	2 paint _brushes_
3 _reels_ of tape	4 _atlases_
4 _plugs_	5 _boxes_ of paper
6 _bags_ of cement	6 _glasses_
List 1	**List 2**

Each of the underlined words in the two shopping lists above is written in the plural. Look carefully at the plural endings of these words.

List 1

We write:
1 pen	but	5 pen<u>s</u>
1 tin	but	2 tin<u>s</u>
1 reel	but	3 reel<u>s</u>
1 plug	but	4 plug<u>s</u>
1 bag	but	6 bag<u>s</u>

List 2

We write:
1 hutch	but	3 hutch<u>es</u>
1 brush	but	2 brush<u>es</u>
1 atlas	but	4 atlas<u>es</u>
1 box	but	5 box<u>es</u>
1 glass	but	6 glass<u>es</u>

Hint

- We add an **'s'** to make most words plural (as in List 1).
- To make words which end in **'ch'**, **'sh'**, **'s'**, **'x'** or **'ss'** plural, we add **'es'** (as in List 2).
- If you say aloud the plural words which end in **'es'**, you can hear the **'es'** endings as an extra syllable or sound part.

  Examples

bus	1 syllable
bus / es	2 syllables
wish	1 syllable
wish / es	2 syllables

Plurals - add 'es'

Over to you

In each phrase below, write the plural of the word shown in **bold**. Look at the ending of each word and follow the guidelines.

one **class** but two
a **fox** but some
an **arch** but three
an **address** but several
one **dish** but four
a **dress** but many
one **church** but six
a **kiss** but lots of
one **peach** but a kilo of
a **bench** but several
a **porch** but two
one **boss** but many

Extra points

▶ In a few words ending in 'o', we also add 'es' to make them plural. These are the most useful examples.

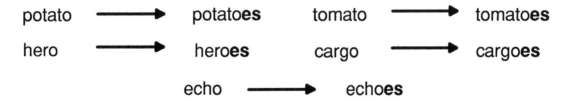

potato ⟶ potato**es**   tomato ⟶ tomato**es**

hero ⟶ hero**es**   cargo ⟶ cargo**es**

echo ⟶ echo**es**

▶ Try grouping the 'es' words together in sentences to help you learn them.
      He eats mang**oes**, tomat**oes** and potat**oes**.
      The mosquit**oes** flew over the volcan**oes**

▶ Remember, we add an **'s'** to most words ending in **'o'** to make them plural.

disco ⟶ disco**s**   piano ⟶ piano**s**

zero ⟶ zero**s**   zoo ⟶ zoo**s**

Plurals - 'f ' and 'fe' words

<table>
<tr><td>

Card 1

roof

café

chief

</td><td>

Card 2

leaf

half

knife

</td></tr>
</table>

► The words on Cards 1 and 2 end in either **'f '** or **'fe'**.
► If we make the words on:
   card 1 plural, we only add **'s'** - roof**s**, café**s**, chief**s**
   card 2 plural, each word will then end in **'ves'** - lea**ves**, hal**ves**, kni**ves**

Hint

* Some words that end in **'f'** or **'fe'**, just have an **'s'** added to make them plural.
  Example   proof   -   proof**s**
* Other words that end in **'f'** or **'fe'**, change to **'ves'** in the plural.
  Example   leaf   -   lea**ves**
* You can usually hear which words end in **'ves'** in the plural.
* When you learn a word which ends **'ves'**, say the word aloud and stress the **'ves'** ending.

Over to you
Highlight the correct spelling from each pair of words. If you have difficulty deciding, check the words in a dictionary.

calfs / calves	halfs / halves
loafs / loaves	lifes / lives
proofs / prooves	shelfs / shelves
thiefs / thieves	wifes / wives
themselfs / themselves	wolfs / wolves

'i' before 'e'

Read these words aloud.
chief
believe
niece
hygiene

▶ You will hear that the letters **'ie'** in each of the words on the card above make a long **'ee'** sound, like the **'E'** at the beginning of **E**gypt.

Hint

◆ People often get confused about whether **'i'** goes before **'e'** in words so:
   1. Test the word to see if the **'ie'** / **'ei'** is making a long **'ee'** sound.
   2. Then remember:
      'i' before **'e'**
      in words with a long **'ee'** sound
   3. This works unless the long **'ee'** sound comes after **'c'** then it's **'ei'**.
      Examples   re**cei**ve   **cei**ling   con**cei**t
   4. Remember this rhyme for these **'ee'** sounding words.
      'i' before **'e'** except after **'c'**

Over to you

1) Follow the guidelines above and complete the spelling of these words. The **'ie'** / **'ei'** in each word makes a long **'ee'** sound.

gr _ _ ve	rec _ _ pt	p _ _ ce	dec _ _ t	conc _ _ ve
dec _ _ tful	rel _ _ f	th _ _ ves	br _ _ f	s _ _ ge

2) Highlight the 10 **'ee'** sounding words in the wordsquare opposite.

8 words go across and 2 go down.

Each word will follow the guidelines in the **Hint** above.

3) Now use in a sentence each **'ie'** / **'ei'** word you have highlighted.

r	r	e	l	i	e	v	e
e	a	c	h	i	e	v	e
c	p	r	i	e	s	t	g
e	z	t	h	i	e	f	r
i	b	e	l	i	e	f	i
v	d	i	e	s	e	l	e
e	d	e	c	e	i	t	f
d	r	e	c	e	i	p	t

'e' before 'i'

► What sound does the 'ei' make in these words?

neighbour
weigh
eighteen

► It makes a long 'a' sound. It's the same sound you hear at the beginning of 'ape' and 'apron'.

Hint

♦ To decide whether you need 'ie' or 'ei' in a word:
    1. Listen to the sound the 'ie' / 'ei' is making.
    2. If you hear a long 'a' sound, you need the letters 'ei'.

Over to you

Match these long 'a' sounding words to their clues. The first one is done for you.

sleigh	the number after 7
reindeer	the sound a horse makes
neigh	pulled by horses or reindeer
eight	an animal with large antlers
reign	blood flows through this
weight	the time a king or queen rules
reins	a colour
beige	scales tell you this
surveillance	straps to guide horses
vein	transport for goods
freight	close observation

'ie' or 'ei'?

The words on this worksheet either:
- ► don't follow the guidelines on pages **33** and **34**

or

- ► the **'ie'** / **'ei'** doesn't make a long **'ee'** or **'a'** sound.

* their heir heiress	an **'air'** sound
* height eiderdown	a long **'i'** sound (as **'i'** in **'ice'**)
* leisure heifer	a short **'e'** sound (as **'e'** in **'egg'**)
* forfeit surfeit	sounds like **'it'** at the end
* field yield shield	the **'ie'** sound is unclear
* veil weir weird	the **'ei'** sound is unclear
* either neither	Do you say these words with a long **'e'** or long **'i'** sound at the beginning?

Hint

- ◆ Group together words that share the same sound (as the words in the table above).
  Example   **ei**ther / n**ei**ther
- ◆ The **'ei'** in **'foreign'** and **'sovereign'** isn't very clear so concentrate on the word **'reign'** at the end of each word and learn the words as a group.   **reign**   fo**reign**   sove**reign**
- ◆ People's names are spelt **'ei'**
  Sh**ei**la N**ei**l D**ei**dre K**ei**th
- ◆ Make up sentences for odd words:
  Counterfeit protein and **caffeine - seize** it!

Over to you

Use the tricky **'ie'** / **'ei'** words on this worksheet in the sentences below. You have been given the first letter of each word. You will have to look back through the worksheet to find the words you need.

a. In t_____ l_____ time they went on f_____ holidays.

b. N_____ boy is an h_____ to his father's millions.

c. I've drunk so much coffee. I've had a s_____ of c_____.

d. At the h_____ of the storm, he covered his head with the e_____.

e. P_____ comes from e_____ meat or fish.

f. The s_____ wore a v_____ at her coronation.

Answers

Vowels page 3

confess	finish
drink	clock
length	shepherd
adult	murder
alphabet	cannot
corner	fantastic
smell	shocking
cobweb	letter

Consonants page 4

yesterday	quick	correct
working	grateful	allow
separate	burglar	beginning
welcome	wonderful	popular
taken	dislike	future
brought	possible	accept
different	danger	children

Base words page 5

forget	weigh	dry
quarrel	enjoy	spell
profit	necessary	polite
listen	obey	satisfy
limit	employ	live
commit	apply	mad
regret	destroy	equal

Syllables page 6

share 1	cancel 2	slippery 3
between 2	prefer 2	tomorrow 3
placing 2	supper 2	every 3
pole 1	claim 1	sandwich 2
chimney 2	family 3	occur 2
responsible 4	wonderful 3	simple 2
managing 3	destination 4	factory 3
finally 3	want 1	foreign 2

Adding prefixes page 7

immature	reappear	unaware
immodest	rearrange	uncertain
impatient	reassure	unnamed
impolite	refuel	unnecessary
impractical	reissue	untidy
improbable	reprint	unusual

One, one, one words page 8

drop	top
snap	strap
hug	shut
win	trip
swim	slim
slid	clap
trim	stop

Doubling a consonant page 10

1)

stripper	spinning
thinnest	sunny
sadder	scarred
dimmer	wettest

2)

scrubbing	stepping
fatten	dragging
padded	muddy

slapping	slimmer
ripped	jammed
skinny	witty
winner	gripped
dropped	grinned
wetter	trapping

No change page 11

spotless, strapless, dimly

skinless, madness, brimful

Dropping an 'e' page 13

1)

grating	grated
closing	closed
arranging	arranged
using	used
chasing	chased
arriving	arrived
deciding	decided
enquiring	enquired
providing	provided
advising	advised
voting	voted
sneezing	sneezed
dancing	danced

2) a. crazy **b.** losing **c.** noisy
d. refusal **e.** inspiring **f.** stony
g. lazy **h.** wasting **i.** writing

Keeping an 'e' page 15

less nameless hopeless blameless
ty safety ninety
ful careful grateful hateful
ment placement amusement excitement
ness politeness
ly bravely sincerely completely lonely

Ending in 'ly' page 16

a. drizzly, **b.** responsibly, **c.** wrinkly,
d. miserably, **e.** probably, **f.** feebly, **g.** gently

'lly' endings page 17

1)

beautifully	gradually
locally	totally
actually	generally
fatally	dreadfully

The letter before 'y' page 18

1)

pray	obey
annoy	boy
buy	valley
play	employ

2) a. try — dry
b. happy — forty
c. easy — lazy
d. satisfy — injury
e. necessary — bury
f. victory — mystery

A vowel before 'y' page 19

obeyed	playful
destroyer	buying

Answers

royalty   employable
prayer   buoyant
enjoyment   surveyor

A consonant before 'y'   page 20

tidies   tidily   tidier   tidiness   tidied
easily   easier
lazily   lazier   laziness
steadies   steadily   steadier   steadiness   steadied
copies   copiable   copier   copied
studies   studied   studious
furious
empties   emptier   emptiness   emptied
heavily   heavier   heaviness

'ing' is different   page 21

envying   hurrying
querying   satisfying
occupying   supplying
denying   replying
flying   applying

Plurals - ends in 'y', add 's'   page 22

1. holidays   6. kidneys
2. chimneys   7. railways
3. jockeys   8. journeys
4. valleys   9. delays
5. monkeys   10. cowboys

Plurals - changing 'y' to 'i'   page 23

1) bodies   parties   mysteries
    cities   properties   centuries
    bullies   factories   opportunities
    skies   supplies   charities
2) berries   libraries
    quantities   armies
    activities   flies
    ferries   countries
    enemies   ladies

Does 'y' change to 'i'?   page 24

1) turkeys   gangways   counties
    twenties   birthdays   hobbies
    pastries   enquiries   victories
2) surveyed   surveying   surveyor
    prettier   prettiest   prettiness
    glorious
    displayed   displaying
    carried   carrier   carrying
    applied   applying
    delayed   delaying
    happily   happiness
    lazily   laziness
    necessarily
    conveyed   conveying   conveyor

Tricky 'y' words   page 25

a. daily   **b.** said   paid   **c.** laid
d. babyhood   **e.** dryness

Adding 'ed'   page 26

happened   returned
listed   crashed
booked   talked

drowned   cleaned
needed   stamped

Single or double?   page 28

1) budgeting   admittance
    offered   limited
    submitting   transferring
    beginner   preferred
    orbited   ordering
2) beginning   credited
    admitted   forbidding
    referred   regrettable
    committed   omitting
    entering   occurred

'l' is different   page 29

1) signalled   cancelled
    marvellous   pedalling
    traveller   patrolled
    totalled   modelling
    quarrelling   labelling

Plurals - add 'es'   page 31

classes   churches
foxes   kisses
arches   peaches
addresses   benches
dishes   porches
dresses   bosses

Plurals - 'f' and 'fe' words   page 32

calves   halves
loaves   lives
proofs   shelves
thieves   wives
themselves   wolves

'i' before 'e'   page 33

1) grieve, receipt, piece, deceit, conceive
    deceitful, relief, thieves, brief, siege
2) **across** relieve, achieve, priest, thief,
           belief, diesel, deceit, receipt
    down received, grief

'e' before 'i'   page 34

reindeer - an animal with large antlers
neigh - the sound a horse makes
eight - the number after 7
reign - the time a king or queen rules
weight - scales tell you this
reins - straps to guide horses
beige - a colour
surveillance - close observation
vein - blood flows through this
freight - transport for goods

'ie' or 'ei'?   page 35

a. their, leisure, foreign
b. Neither, heir
c. surfeit, caffeine
d. height, eiderdown
e. protein, either
f. sovereign, veil

MCH Publications

Other series at Foundation Level

Foundation Communication Assignments:
Health & Social Care
Leisure & Tourism
Business

The books in this series cover the requirements of the Core Skills Communication Unit at Level 1 by allowing students to practise their skills in a vocational context.

Introducing Core Communication

Complements the Foundation Communication Assignments series by providing guidance and practice in the underpinning generic communication skills.

Intermediate Level series

Core Skills Communication Assignments:
Health & Social Care
Leisure & Tourism
Business
Hospitality & Catering

The books in this series cover the requirements of the Core Skills Communication Unit at Level 2 by allowing students to practise their skills in a vocational context.

Developing Core Communication Skills

Complements the Core Skills Communication Assignments series by providing guidance and practice in the underpinning generic communication skills.